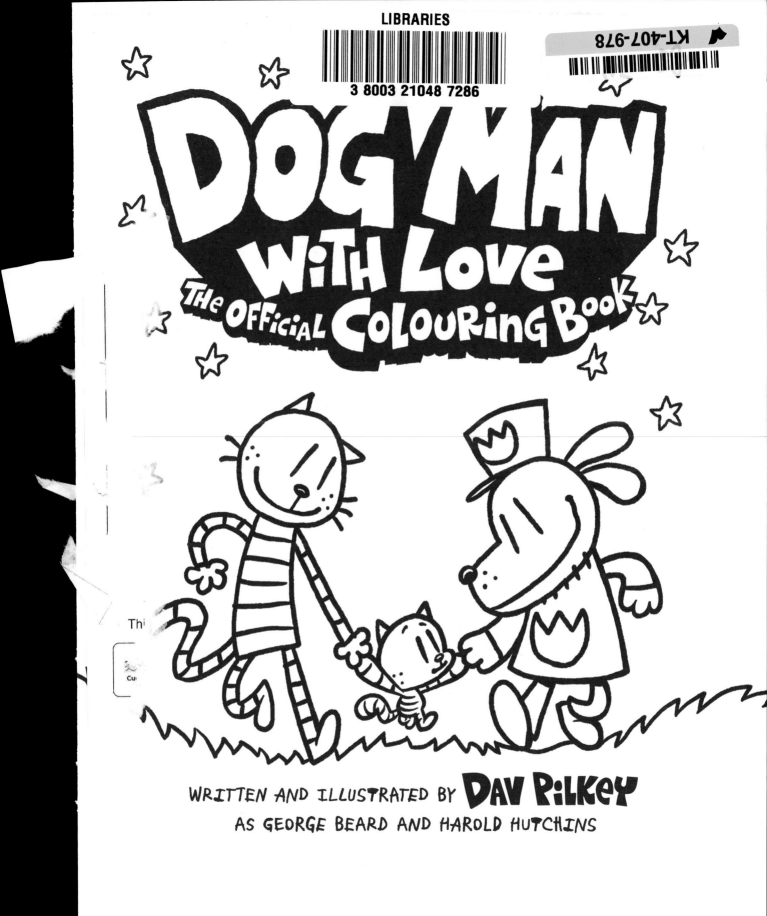

DOG MAN
WITH LOVE
THE OFFICIAL COLOURING BOOK

WRITTEN AND ILLUSTRATED BY **DAV PILKEY**

AS GEORGE BEARD AND HAROLD HUTCHINS

SCHOLASTIC

Published in the UK by Scholastic, 2023
1 London Bridge, London, SE1 9BG
Scholastic Ireland, 89E Lagan Road, Dublin Industrial Estate, Glasnevin, Dublin, D11 HP5F

SCHOLASTIC and associated logos are trademarks and/or
registered trademarks of Scholastic Inc.

First published in the US by Scholastic Inc, 2023

ISBN 978 07023 3014 8

A CIP catalogue record for this book is available from the British Library.

Page 10: 1 Corinthians 13:4 (English Standard Version)
Page 12: 1 Corinthians 13:7 (New International Version)
Page 15: 1 Corinthians 13:7 (English Standard Version)
Page 16: 1 Corinthians 13:13 (English Standard Version)

Printed by Bell and Bain Limited, Glasgow
Paper made from wood grown in sustainable forests and other controlled sources.

3 5 7 9 10 8 6 4 2

www.scholastic.co.uk
www.pilkey.com

Dear readers,

When I made the first DoG Man book in 2016, my goal was to write a love letter to dogs. By the third book, I found I was writing a love letter to my parents.

I have just finished writing and illustrating the eleventh Dog Man book, and I never dreamed that topics such as destiny, grief, death, forgiveness, and redemption would find their way into these books.

I never quite know where these tales will take me. But my hope is that every book will, at the end of the day, still be a story about love.

I hope you enjoy filling this book up with colours, and may all of <u>Your</u> stories be stories about love.

Love is patient and Kind...

1 Corinthians 13:4

... Love believes all things,
hopes all things,
endures all things.

1 Corinthians 13:7

...faith, hope, and love abide,
these three;
but the greatest of these is love.

1 Corinthians 13:13

We're NOT Just GONNA **BE GOOD...**

We're GONNA **DO GOOD!**

But my mother always forgave me...

...even after she passed away.

...and never Giving up hope.

Yeah, but it wasn't **ALL** bad.

At least I got to hold your hand.

...love costs all we are
and will ever be.
Yet it is only love
which sets us free.

—Maya Angelou

A loving heart is better and stronger than wisdom.

~Charles Dickens

You are my sun, my moon, and all of my stars.

—e. e. cummings

Is she here, too, Papa?

Well...

...It's **YOUR** story, kid.

Not all of us
can do great things,
but we can do small things
with great love.

—Attributed to Mother Teresa

Forever and ever!

There is no remedy for love but to love more.

—Henry David Thoreau